publications international, ltd.

Carl Fredricksen is a lonely old man.

Carl has always wanted to travel to South America, like his childhood hero, explorer Charles Muntz. But the years went past, and he never made it there.

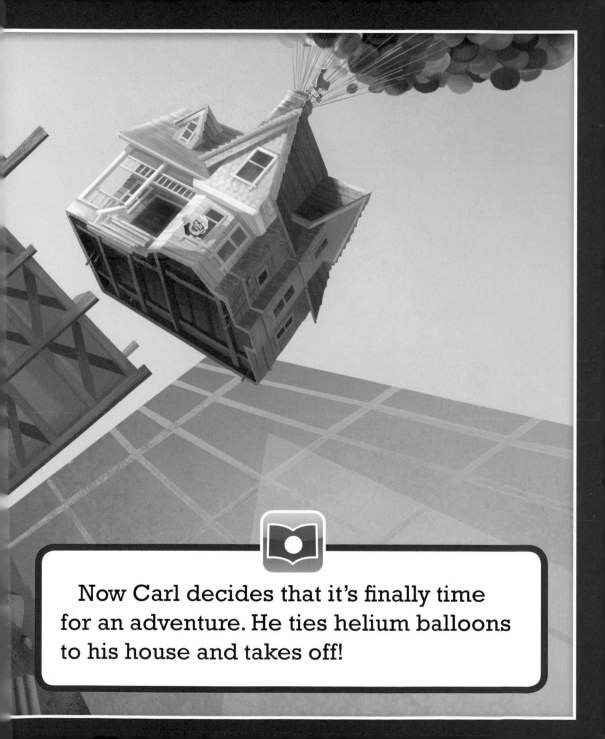

Now Carl decides that it's finally time for an adventure. He ties helium balloons to his house and takes off!

Then Carl finds a stowaway — a helpful Junior Wilderness Explorer named Russell. Russell steers the house through a big storm, all the way to South America.

The house lands near the spot where Carl wants to live. Carl and Russell pull the house closer, like a big parade balloon.

Along the way, Carl and Russell meet a friendly dog named Dug.

Together they make another new friend—a big, strange mama bird. Russell names her Kevin.

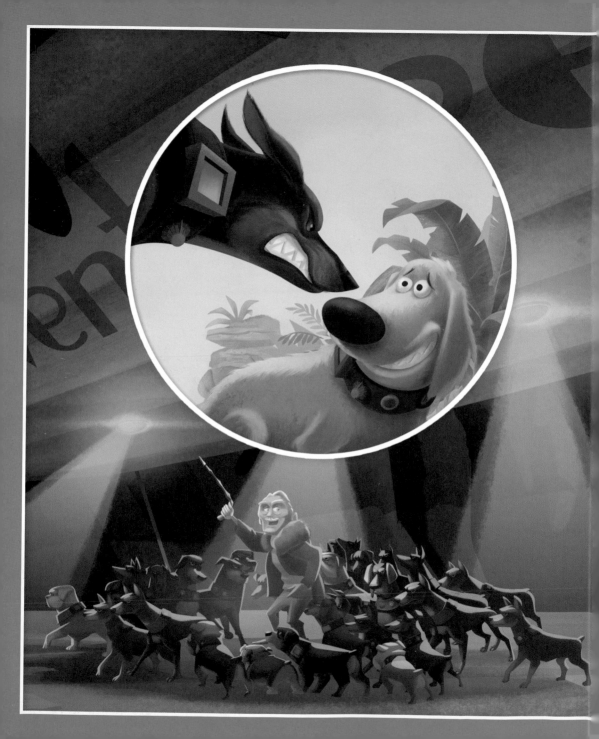

Then Dug's packmates Alpha, Beta, and Gamma show up. They aren't friendly like Dug. The dogs take Carl and Russell to their mysterious master, who turns out to be Carl's old hero, Charles Muntz!

Muntz has changed, and not for the better. He wants Kevin for his animal collection, and he would do *anything*—to *anyone*—to capture her.